THE ODYSSEY
A GREEK PLAY FOR STUDENTS

ORIGINALLY BY HOMER
ADAPTATED BY BRENT SUDDUTH
ILLUSTRATED BY ERIN EITTER KONO

MONDO

For information contact:

MONDO Publishing
980 Avenue of the Americas
New York, NY 10018

Visit our website at http://www.mondopub.com

Printed in USA

07 08 09 10 11   9 8 7 6 5 4 3 2 1

ISBN 1-59034-812-5

Designed by Witz End Design

CONTENTS

INTRODUCTION

"The play's the thing," speaks Hamlet in William Shakespeare's play of the same name. Hamlet goes on to describe how, with help from a traveling theater group, he plans to reenact what he believes happened to his father. Plays allow the unbelievable to come to life in exciting and creative ways.

That's why plays are great teaching tools. Students can pretend they are living in other times, places, and cultures. Plays can challenge students to see the world in a different way. Plays can also improve students' reading and comprehension skills, and, because plays are meant to be spoken aloud, students' oral language skills as well. Most importantly, while reading tends to be a solitary activity, plays turn reading into a social and active endeavor. All students participate either as performers or as audience members.

Unlike plays with limited numbers of parts, this version of *The Odyssey* has many different characters and settings. This means there is a part for anyone who wants one, even if your class is large. This play is flexible and will accommodate the needs of almost any size classroom. Shy students can take on smaller parts or work behind the scenes helping with set design, direction, or costumes. More confident students can take on more than one part, which will give them a broader understanding of the story's language, characters, and plot. This version of the play has minimal stage directions—noted in parentheses and in italics— so you and your students can be creative and come up with your own interpretation. Because many of the character names and settings might be challenging to your students, a pronunciation guide is included at the end of the book.

Below are some basic guidelines on how to go about putting on this play, but there really isn't any right or wrong way to do it. The most important thing is to have fun and be creative. Everyone—teacher included—should *play* with it!

PERFORMING THE PLAY WITH A SMALL GROUP OF STUDENTS

This play can be performed with a minimum of eight students, as long as each student is willing to play more than one role. Some scenes are supposed to have large groups in them, but as long as you have enough students for the key parts then the play will flow. For example, when Odysseus speaks to his crew on board his ship, it's essential only that there are enough students to play Odysseus and the Sailors who have lines—and if need be, one person can even play all of the Sailors! Having many Sailors isn't necessary to convey the spirit and mood of a ship voyage. Another example comes early in the play when the Suitors are introduced. If necessary, one student can play all the Suitors. It's up to you how you handle your students playing multiple characters, and it will depend on what best suits the size of your classroom.

PERFORMING THE PLAY WITH A LARGE GROUP OF STUDENTS

This version of *The Odyssey* has more than 40 parts, so if you are working with a large group, there will be a role for everyone. Even if you have more students than there are speaking roles, no one needs to be left out. For example, the character Athena disguises herself as various characters throughout the play, so in order to accommodate more students, different kids could play Athena in her different disguises. How you go about staging the play (see below) could also increase the number of roles.

STAGING, COSTUMES, AND PROPS

Performing a play is much more than speaking lines; it's also physically acting out the part in front of an audience, and interacting with fellow actors. *The Odyssey* can be staged in different ways, depending on the kind of play you and your students want to perform.

For example, because the part of Charybdis, the great whirlpool, doesn't have any lines, this character could be portrayed by a set piece that students could create. However, another way would be to have a few students play Charybdis by moving and spinning around the stage, pretending to be a giant whirlpool. These two approaches will give you very different results.

Costumes can be as elaborate or as simple as you and your students want. If your group is small and each student will be playing multiple parts, then having costumes that are difficult to change in and out of might prove problematic. In this case, having one key item—a vest or a certain type of hat, for example—to identify a character might be the way to go. However, if you have a large group where each student will have just one part, then the costumes could be more elaborate.

The decision about the type and number of props you use will also depend on the size of your group and the amount of time you will devote to putting on the play. Whatever props you decide to use should be easy and safe for children to handle.

The staging, costumes, and props you choose will depend on the amount of time you plan to devote to the play, the interest shown by your students, the size of the group, and whether or not you have any funds to work with. Just remember: have fun with it!

Places Everyone! Hurry!

Director

CAST OF CHARACTERS
(IN ORDER OF APPEARANCE)

HOMER

CALLIOPE

ODYSSEUS

ATHENA

NARRATOR

HOMER, Author and poet

CALLIOPE, Muse

TELEMACHUS, Odysseus's son

PENELOPE, Odysseus's wife

ANTINOUS, AMPHINOMUS, EURYMACHUS, Suitors who want Penelope's hand in marriage

ATHENA, Patron Goddess of Athens who watches over Odysseus

KING NESTOR, King of Pylos

PISISTRATUS, King Nestor's son

KING MENELAUS, King of Sparta

QUEEN HELEN, Menelaus's wife, whose capture started the Trojan War

ZEUS, King of the Gods

HERMES, Messenger of the Gods

ODYSSEUS, Hero of the story

CALYPSO, Sea Nymph

INO, Sea Nymph

PRINCESS NAUSICAA, Princess
of the Phaeacians

HANDMAIDENS, of Nausicaa

KING ALCINOUS, King of the Phaeacians

QUEEN ARETE, Queen of the Phaeacians

DEMODOCUS, Blind bard of the Phaeacians

EURYALUS, Athletic youth of the Phaeacians

SAILORS, of Odysseus's ship

PEOPLE OF CICONS

POLYPHEMUS, Cyclops and Poseidon's son

OTHER CYCLOPES

AEOLUS, Ruler of Winds

GIANTS, from Laestrygonia

CIRCE, of Aeaea

TIRESIAS, Blind prophet

SIRENS, Women who sing a dangerous song

SCYLLA, Six-headed monster

CHARYBDIS, Great whirlpool

THE SUN

EUMAEUS, Shepherd of Ithaca and family
friend of Odysseus

PIRAEUS, Sailor

ARNAEUS, Beggar

MELANTHO, Maidservant to Penelope

EURYCLEIA, Penelope's handmaiden

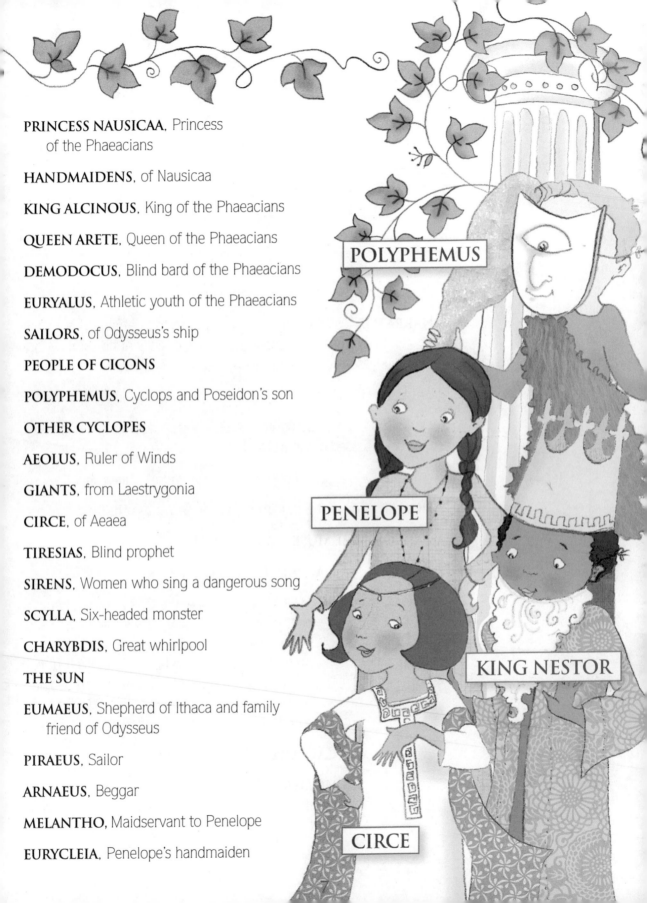

POLYPHEMUS

PENELOPE

KING NESTOR

CIRCE

7

THE PLAY BEGINS

(Lights up. The NARRATOR stands on the stage.)

NARRATOR We humbly welcome you to this gathering as we tell the tale of one of the greatest heroes of ancient times: the story of Odysseus! Welcome to—*The Odyssey*!

(Enter HOMER.)

This is Homer. He wrote *The Odyssey* by collecting the stories orally passed down from person to person.

(CALLIOPE appears holding a sign with "Muse" written on it.)

HOMER The first thing I'm going to need is a—oh, there you are.

CALLIOPE THE MUSE *(Waving.)* Hi!

NARRATOR Who is that?

HOMER She's Calliope, the Greek muse of epic poetry—one of the nine Muses that inspire and help people in literature, the arts, and science. An epic poem is a long poem that tells a story. *The Odyssey* is set during a time when people believed in the Greek gods—over 3,000 years ago. So it's only right that I ask her to inspire me.

CALLIOPE May I help you?

HOMER Well, I have a long story to tell about the great hero Odysseus, but I'm not really sure how to begin.

CALLIOPE *(Thinking.)* Hmm…. When Odysseus left home to fight in the Trojan War, his only son, Telemachus, was just a baby. But 20 years later, Telemachus has grown up. Maybe you should begin with him.

HOMER Now that's inspiration!

NARRATOR Wait a minute, why begin with his son?

CALLIOPE I have a very good reason. You'll see.

(CALLIOPE exits. HOMER hands NARRATOR a stack of signs, each one representing one of the books of The Odyssey. *He nudges NARRATOR to show the first one—"Book 1." NARRATOR holds up "Book 1" sign and continues to show the card corresponding to each book as HOMER announces them throughout the play.)*

HOMER Book 1!

NARRATOR *(Indicating sign.)* This isn't a book, it's just a sign that says "Book 1."

HOMER Yes, yes, I know, but when I write my stories, I break them up into different sections, called "books." Think of them as chapters.

NARRATOR Oh, okay. *(Turns to audience.)* Our story begins in Ithaca, Odysseus's homeland. His wife, Penelope, awaits his return from the Trojan War. And his son, Telemachus, just an infant when Odysseus left, is all grown up now.

(HOMER and NARRATOR exit.)

(Dinnertime. Enter PENELOPE, who sits at the dinner table. TELEMACHUS enters and sits down at the table with his mother.)

TELEMACHUS Hey Mom, is Dad home yet?

PENELOPE Not yet. But he said he'd be right back.

TELEMACHUS That was 20 years ago, Mom.

PENELOPE   I know. It just gets harder and harder to keep his dinner warm every day. Eat your peas, Telemachus.

TELEMACHUS   Think of all the peas I'm saving from a horrible death in my stomach.

(SUITORS enter from the side of stage. They whisper amongst themselves, look at PENELOPE, and wave to her.)

Hey, Mom, are you ever going to tell these guys hanging around the palace that just because Dad isn't back yet, it doesn't mean you're going to marry one of them?

(SUITORS exit.)

PENELOPE   Well, I don't want to be rude.

TELEMACHUS   But they are so annoying!

PENELOPE   Eat your peas, Telemachus, and let me handle our guests.

(HOMER and NARRATOR enter, followed by ATHENA.)

HOMER   Enter...Athena!

NARRATOR   Wow, she looks great.

ATHENA   Of course I look great. I am a goddess!

HOMER   Athena is Zeus's daughter and the goddess of wisdom, battle, and womanly arts. Her favorite city is Athens, of course. She likes Odysseus and watches over him as best she can throughout his journeys.

(HOMER and NARRATOR exit. PENELOPE moves to side stage.)

ATHENA   Since no one knows where Odysseus is, I will help Telemachus find him. I'll disguise myself and help him secretly.

(TELEMACHUS finishes his meal and leaves the table while ATHENA disguises herself as MENTES, an old friend of ODYSSEUS.)

ATHENA AS MENTES   Hello there, young man.

TELEMACHUS   Mentes! How good to see one of my father's best friends.

ATHENA AS MENTES How are you?

TELEMACHUS Pretty good, except for the whole "missing Dad" thing, you know?

ATHENA AS MENTES I bet your father will be home sooner than you think. Maybe you should sail to some other cities and see if there is any news of his whereabouts.

TELEMACHUS That's a great idea!

ATHENA AS MENTES Yes, but don't tell your mother why you're going—because then, if you do find your father, you can surprise her. But first, tell those suitors…

TELEMACHUS *(Interrupting ATHENA AS MENTES.)* Suitors?

ATHENA AS MENTES Yes, suitors.

TELEMACHUS "Suitors" is a pretty funny word, isn't it?

ATHENA AS MENTES I never thought about it…but anyway, tell those guys to pack their bags and leave. They're up to no good and they're bothering your mother. *(ATHENA exits.)*

TELEMACHUS You're right! *(SUITORS appear.)*

Hey, you! Suitors! Pack your bags and stop bothering my mom. And stop eating all my banana chips!

ANTINOUS We couldn't possibly leave.

AMPHINOMUS Your father isn't here and someone needs to rule Ithaca!

EURYMACHUS Might as well be me.

AMPHINOMUS Or me.

ALL SUITORS Or me!

TELEMACHUS Well, I'm sailing to Pylos and Sparta, and you'd better be gone by the time I get back!

ANTINOUS Banana chips anyone?

(The SUITORS move off to the side and stand around, eating. Enter HOMER and NARRATOR.)

BOOK 2

HOMER Book 2! *(To NARRATOR.)* Where's the sign?

NARRATOR It's coming, it's coming.

(NARRATOR holds up the "Book 2" sign. HOMER and NARRATOR move off to the side of the stage.)

TELEMACHUS *(To PENELOPE.)* Mom, I'm off to find—uh, I mean, I'm going on a trip. I'll be back in a little while. Wish me luck!

PENELOPE Have a safe trip, Telemachus. Try not to take as long as your father. I can't keep all this food warm much longer.

(She sits down and starts weaving a cloth.)

TELEMACHUS I'll be back as soon as I can.

(Enter ATHENA AS MENTOR.)

HOMER Enter…Athena!

NARRATOR Athena is disguised as another old friend of Odysseus's.

TELEMACHUS Hi, Mentor! I'm sailing off to find my dad.

ATHENA AS MENTOR Sounds like fun. Can I go?

TELEMACHUS It would be great if you could come with me, but I'm a bit worried about my mom and those suitors. Would you mind staying and keeping an eye on them?

(SUITORS enter from the side of the stage and wave to PENELOPE as she sits and weaves. They are clearly impatient.)

ATHENA AS MENTOR *(Laughs.)* I'd be happy to if I thought it was necessary, but don't worry, your mother will be fine. She's a smart lady, you know. Remember that time she told the suitors she'd pick one of them just as soon as she finished weaving a cloth? *(Laughs again.)* What she didn't tell them was that each morning she unravels what she wove the night before.

TELEMACHUS So she'll never finish the cloth?

ATHENA AS MENTOR Exactly. The suitors will have to wait a very long time for her indeed. *(PENELOPE and SUITORS exit.)*

BOOK 3

(NARRATOR holds up "Book 3" sign.)

HOMER Book 3!

(TELEMACHUS and ATHENA AS MENTOR on a ship, landing at the port city of Pylos.)

NARRATOR Telemachus and Athena (still disguised as Mentor) sail to Pylos, where a great feast and celebration is taking place.

(Enter KING NESTOR. HOMER and NARRATOR exit.)

KING NESTOR Now who might you be?

TELEMACHUS Greetings, King Nestor. I'm Telemachus, son of Odysseus.

KING NESTOR You mean the big guy who had the idea for the giant wooden horse that helped us win the war in Troy?

TELEMACHUS Right. I'm the son of the big guy.

KING NESTOR Well, welcome, Telemachus! Come join us as we celebrate Poseidon, King of the Sea! What can I do for you?

ATHENA AS MENTOR Go on, ask him.

TELEMACHUS I was hoping you could tell me where my father is.

KING NESTOR Your father was a great warrior, but I have not seen him since I left Troy. He stayed behind with Agamemnon while I returned home. Agamemnon's brother, King Menelaus, left Troy around the same time I did. I want to help you, Telemachus, so I shall ask my son, Pisistratus, to join your search party. Go to Sparta and speak with Menelaus. Maybe he knows something.

(Enter PISISTRATUS.)

PISISTRATUS Woo-hoo! Road trip!

TELEMACHUS Actually, it's a chariot trip.

ATHENA AS MENTOR Thank you, King Nestor. And now, I must go!

(ATHENA AS MENTOR changes into an eagle and flies away.)

KING NESTOR Did that old man just change into an eagle?

PISISTRATUS Cool!

KING NESTOR Athena is watching over you, Telemachus. Be well in your journey!

(TELEMACHUS and PISISTRATUS get on a chariot and exit.)

(Enter HOMER and NARRATOR. NARRATOR holds up "Book 4" sign.)

HOMER Here we go into Book 4!

(Enter TELEMACHUS and PISISTRATUS on chariot.)

NARRATOR Telemachus and Pisistratus ride onward to—hmm, maybe we should first explain what they're riding on?

HOMER Well, this story takes place sometime around the twelfth century B C. The only ways to travel over land back then were on foot, on horseback, or on a small, two-wheeled, horse-pulled cart, called a chariot—which is what Telemachus and Pisistratus take.

NARRATOR Telemachus and Pisistratus ride to Sparta, where they find King Menelaus.

HOMER And Helen, his wife.

NARRATOR Helen? Wasn't she the cause of the Trojan War?

HOMER Well, sort of. You see, there was this wedding…all the gods and goddesses were invited except for Eris, goddess of discord. She was so angry about not being invited that she threw a golden apple into the wedding crowd with a note saying, "For the Fairest." Three goddesses wanted the apple—Aphrodite, Hera, and Athena—but they couldn't decide who should get it. So Zeus suggested that Paris, a mortal man from Troy, choose which goddess was fairest. Paris gave the apple to Aphrodite, and to thank him she promised him the most beautiful woman in the world: Helen.

NARRATOR But wasn't Helen already married?

HOMER Yes, which is why the war began. Aphrodite stole Helen from King Menelaus and gave her to Paris. King Menelaus and some others chose to fight against the Trojans to get her back. The war lasted ten years, until the Trojans were defeated and Helen was returned. I wrote about this in another epic poem—*The Iliad.*

(Enter KING MENELAUS and QUEEN HELEN, who admires her reflection in a hand mirror the whole time she's on stage. HOMER and NARRATOR move to side of stage. TELEMACHUS and PISISTRATUS get off chariot.)

TELEMACHUS Great King Menelaus, I'm sorry to interrupt the wedding celebrations of your son and daughter, but you wouldn't happen to know where my father is, would you?

KING MENELAUS I wouldn't know where your father is because I have no idea who your father is.

TELEMACHUS My father is Odysseus. I'm his son, Telemachus.

KING MENELAUS Ah, yes, Odysseus, the great warrior. I haven't seen him since I left the city of Troy.

TELEMACHUS Aww...I'm never going to find him.

KING MENELAUS But—

TELEMACHUS But?

KING MENELAUS But, I had a difficult time finding my way home, until Proteus, the Old Man of the Sea, helped me. And he happened to tell me that your father was on an island, being held captive by the sea nymph, Calypso.

TELEMACHUS My father is alive! Thank you! This news will make my mother extremely happy!

(Exit TELEMACHUS and PISISTRATUS on chariot, and KING MENELAUS. Enter SUITORS and PENELOPE, who is listening in on the SUITORS.)

NARRATOR Meanwhile back in Ithaca, those sneaky suitors get sneakier.

ANTINOUS What happens if Telemachus finds out that Odysseus is alive?

AMPHINOMUS We'll stop him before he is able to get back and tell Penelope!

EURYMACHUS Banana chips, anyone?

PENELOPE My son is searching for my husband? And these suitors want to stop him from reaching me? I must do something!

(Enter ATHENA disguised as IPHTHIME.)

HOMER Enter...Athena!

NARRATOR This time she is disguised as Penelope's sister, Iphthime.

ATHENA AS IPHTHIME   Don't worry, Penelope, your son is going
to be just fine.

PENELOPE   How do you know, Iphthime? And by the way,
that's an amazing pair of sandals you're wearing.

ATHENA AS IPHTHIME   Why, thank you.
A little bird told me—more like an eagle,
actually—that Telemachus will be safe
from those devious, crafty suitors.
(She winks.)

PENELOPE   Those suitors really are
annoying, aren't they?

ATHENA AS IPHTHIME   So annoying.
(Exit PENELOPE.)

(NARRATOR indicates "Book 5" sign.)

HOMER   Book 5!

(All the GODS and GODDESSES enter.)

NARRATOR   Athena calls a meeting of all the gods and goddesses to
ask if they can help Odysseus. With Zeus's approval, all agree to
free him. All but one, that is: Poseidon, god of the sea, isn't at the
meeting at all.

ZEUS   As king of the gods, I send Hermes, messenger of the gods, to
tell Calypso that she must free Odysseus.

*(All the GODS and GODDESSES clap as ODYSSEUS and CALYPSO
appear. They are playing a game of chess. ODYSSEUS is very bored, but
CALYPSO is having a great time.)*

CALYPSO   Oooo…check!

HERMES   *(Speaking very quickly.)*   HeythereCalypsoHiOdysseusCalypso
youmustfreehimZeus'sorders!

CALYPSO   Do you know what he said?

(ODYSSEUS shakes his head "no.")

Could you say that a little slower, please?

HERMES Sorry about that. Hey there, Calypso. Hi, Odysseus. Calypso, you must free him. Zeus's orders!

CALYPSO Free Odysseus? He washed up on my island after his ship sunk and I took care of him. Besides, we happen to be right in the middle of this really great game of—

(HERMES waves his finger at CALYPSO.)

Oh, all right. You're free, Odysseus. I'll get you a boat and some food.

ODYSSEUS Whew! That was the longest chess game ever. And by the way, checkmate!

CALYPSO Not fair! Not fair! We minor goddesses always get the short end of the stick! *(She stomps off.)*

NARRATOR Excuse me for just a moment. This story is called *The Odyssey*, right? After Odysseus?

HOMER Yes.

NARRATOR So why are we just now seeing him?

HOMER Remember what my muse suggested? All epic poems have a central hero and almost always start *in medias res*—which means "in the middle of things" in Latin. Odysseus is the central hero, but instead of starting at the beginning of his journey, I started long after he'd begun his travels home.

NARRATOR Right in the middle of his troubles! So that's why you started with Telemachus!

HOMER Exactly.

(ODYSSEUS is on his ship and sailing.)

HOMER Eighteen days into his journey home, Odysseus reaches Scheria, the island of the Phaeacians. Just as Odysseus is about to make landfall, trouble begins. Remember the one god missing at that big meeting?

NARRATOR You mean Poseidon, King of the Seas?

HOMER Yes. Well, Odysseus made Poseidon angry a few years back. But you'll see—that part is coming up soon enough.

NARRATOR Uh-oh. Sounds like Odysseus is in big trouble.

(ODYSSEUS'S ship is rocked by a huge storm.)

HOMER Poseidon has no idea why, but he realizes that all the other gods have set Odysseus free. He's so angry that he creates a huge ocean storm that destroys Odysseus's ship just as he's about to reach Scheria. Enter—

(INO appears.)

NARRATOR Athena!

(INO looks confused.)

HOMER Um, no. At least not yet. Enter…Ino!

INO *(Nodding and smiling.)* Hi! I'm a sea nymph like Calypso. Odysseus, take this veil of mine and tie it around your body. It will help you stay afloat in this terrible storm.

(ODYSSEUS ties the veil around him as he swims .)

ODYSSEUS Whoa! The water is really deep here!

(Athena appears.)

HOMER Enter—

ATHENA Athena, yeah, yeah, we know. STOP!

(Athena makes a "stop" sign with her hand, and the storm stops. Then she checks her hair, patting it.)

Whew! All that wind messed up my hair. I'm doing my best to keep Odysseus safe, but…

ODYSSEUS *(Flailing in the water.)* Help! Help!

NARRATOR Odysseus calls out to all the gods for help.

HOMER A river on the isle of Scheria "hears" his plea and allows Odysseus to swim safely to the island and to go upstream.

(Odysseus crawls onto land.)

INO May I have my veil back, please?

ODYSSEUS *(Handing the veil to her, still on his knees.)* Thank you, Ino. Boy, am I exhausted after all of that! I need a nap.

(He lies down and goes to sleep.)

BOOK 6

(NARRATOR shows the "Book 6" sign.)

HOMER Book 6! The island of Scheria is home to the Phaeacians—the largest tribe of Greek people that lived during this time.

(NAUSICAA enters, lies down on a bed, and falls asleep.)

NARRATOR While Odysseus sleeps, Athena goes to the palace of the Phaeacians on a mission. At the palace, Nausicaa, a Phaeacian princess, is in her bedroom, having a vivid dream.

HOMER Enter—

(ATHENA enters, disguised as Nausicaa's friend. HOMER and NARRATOR exit.)

ATHENA AS NAUSICAA'S FRIEND *(To audience.)* Guess who? Since I'm in the neighborhood, I thought I'd disguise myself as Nausicaa's friend and say hello to her.

PRINCESS NAUSICAA *(Still asleep and dreaming.)*   Where am I?

ATHENA AS NAUSICAA'S FRIEND You're dreaming, princess.

PRINCESS NAUSICAA I know you, don't I?

ATHENA AS NAUSICAA'S FRIEND Of course you do. I'm your friend, princess. I'm just here to suggest that when you wake up, you go down to the river to wash your clothes so you'll be ready for the big celebration tomorrow. You never know who—I mean, *what*—you might find there.

PRINCESS NAUSICAA That's a great idea!

ATHENA AS NAUSICAA'S FRIEND Nighty-night.

(Athena exits.)

PRINCESS NAUSICAA *(Waking up.)*   What a beautiful morning! What a strange dream. I think I'll go down to the river and wash my clothes to make sure I'm the prettiest princess at the celebration later. Besides, you never know who—I mean, *what*—I might find there!

(NARRATOR enters.)

NARRATOR Nausicaa and her handmaidens go down to the river, wash clothes, and then set them out to dry.

(ODYSSEUS is still sleeping nearby, but NAUSICAA and her handmaidens don't see him. NARRATOR moves to side of stage.)

ODYSSEUS *(Waking.)*   Boy, was I tired!

(ODYSSEUS stands and the girls scream at the sight him. ODYSSEUS screams back.)

PRINCESS NAUSICAA Who are you?

ODYSSEUS Who are you?

PRINCESS NAUSICAA *(Regally.)*   I am Princess Nausicaa. Why are you spying on us?

ODYSSEUS I wasn't spying on you. Actually, I just woke up. My name is—   *(pauses)*   I am but a passing traveler, kind princess.

My ship was wrecked in a terrible storm, and I landed on this lovely island. I'm tired and need help getting home. Can you help me out?

PRINCESS NAUSICAA Hmm...I suppose so.

(She waves her hand in front of her nose.)

But I think you need a bath first.

(ODYSSEUS jumps in the water and starts splashing water on himself.)

PRINCESS NAUSICAA Here, you'll need these, too.

(A HANDMAIDEN hands NAUSICAA some clothes, which she tosses in ODYSSEUS's direction. Her back is turned, she isn't looking at ODYSSEUS. He puts on the clothes.)

PRINCESS NAUSICAA And another thing—

(ODYSSEUS walks over to NAUSICAA. He looks amazing.)

ODYSSEUS Yes, princess?

NAUSICAA *(Swooning.)* Oh, wow.

(ODYSSEUS is smiling, waiting for her to continue speaking.)

Umm...oh, yeah...if you walk that way, you'll get to the palace. But you can't walk with me or else people will gossip. Find me at the celebration later, and then you can ask my parents for help. But ask my mom first—she's the nice one.

ODYSSEUS Okay, thanks, Princess.

(NAUSICAA exits. ATHENA enters, disguised as a little girl, followed by HOMER.)

BOOK 7

HOMER If Athena is entering, then you know what that means. Book 7!

(NARRATOR shows "Book 7" sign. HOMER and NARRATOR exit. ODYSSEUS starts walking and sees ATHENA AS LITTLE GIRL.)

ODYSSEUS Excuse me, is this the way to the palace?

ATHENA AS LITTLE GIRL Yes it is, kind sir. Let me show you the way.

(She takes his hand.)

NARRATOR The people of Scheria tend to be wary of strangers, so Athena surrounds Odysseus and herself in a protective mist and guides him into the palace where the festival is taking place.

(Enter KING ALCINOUS and QUEEN ARETE. ODYSSEUS gets down on his knees in front of QUEEN ARETE. The mist fades away.)

ODYSSEUS Oh, great queen, hear my plea!

(Both the KING and QUEEN look shocked.)

KING ALCINOUS Did you see that, my dear? This man just appeared at your feet out of nowhere! Are you a god, sir?

ODYSSEUS Oh no, great King Alcinous. I am but a lowly mortal… a soldier, actually, who has traveled long and hard. I'm returning home after fighting in the Trojan War. My ship was lost at sea, and I barely made it to the shores of your great land. I humbly ask for your help in returning home.

KING ALCINOUS Well, of course, soldier, we'd be glad to help. I can send you home on a ship tomorrow, if you'd like.

QUEEN ARETE I like your taste in clothes, soldier, but I think those belong to my daughter.

KING ALCINOUS What?!

ODYSSEUS I can explain. I was so tired after my journey that I fell asleep by the river. I met your daughter there this morning…she was doing laundry. She kindly gave me these clothes so I could look my best for you. She asked me to come back with her but I told her such a beautiful princess shouldn't be seen with a lowly soldier like me.

KING ALCINOUS Impressive! None of those creeps Nausicaa dates would have thought of that. So before you go, you must marry my daughter.

ODYSSEUS Huh?

KING ALCINOUS I insist.

BOOK 8

(Enter HOMER and NARRATOR. NARRATOR shows "Book 8" sign.)

HOMER Book 8! Wherein our hero tries not to reveal his true identity.

NARRATOR King Alcinous asks his counselors for permission to give a ship to this godlike stranger. The counselors agree, so the Phaeacians get a ship ready for Odysseus, who they think is a brave soldier. They have a big celebration in his honor. .

(Enter DEMODOCUS, EURYALUS, and other PHAEACIANS. The party begins. DEMODOCUS, a blind storyteller, begins playing a lyre—an instrument like a small harp.)

KING ALCINOUS We Phaeacians like to play games, stranger. Will you join in on a little boxing? A little discus throwing?

ODYSSEUS *(Looking and sounding very sad.)* Thank you, King, but I think I'll pass.

EURYALUS I'll bet he's afraid of how strong I am!

ODYSSEUS *(Rising to the challenge.)* I'd never be afraid of a boy like you!

(ODYSSEUS and some youths, including EURYALUS, compete in a few games. ODYSSEUS beats them at every contest.)

KING ALCINOUS Spectacular! I bet you've worked up quite an appetite from those contests. Eat! Maybe these young whippersnappers can impress you with a song and dance instead.

ODYSSEUS Perhaps Demodocus could sing of how we beat the Trojans in the war?

KING ALCINOUS   Of course. Demodocus, if you please.

(DEMODOCUS begins to play his lyre, and just before he starts to sing ODYSSEUS begins weeping.)

Stop! Stop!   *(Waves his arms in the air.)*   Stranger, every time Demodocus plays you get so sad. Is he hurting your ears?

ODYSSEUS   No, it is not him, but what he sings about.

DEMODOCUS   But I haven't sung anything yet.

ODYSSEUS   *(Weeping further.)*   Yes, but I know what you are going to sing about.

KING ALCINOUS   I think it's time for you to tell us exactly who you are, stranger.

HOMER   Oh, this is good stuff! Book 9! Hey, why aren't you holding the sign up?

NARRATOR   *(Holding up sign for "Book 9.")*   I'm holding, I'm holding!

ODYSSEUS   My name is…Odysseus.

(Gasps are heard and "ODYSSEUS" is whispered by everyone.)

I am on my way home to Ithaca to see my wife and son. I haven't been home in over 20 years.

PRINCESS NAUSICAA   *(Looking disappointed.)*   I'm not getting married after all, am I?

QUEEN ARETE   I don't think so, dear.

KING ALCINOUS   The legendary Odysseus? Fierce warrior? Creator of the Trojan horse that brought down the city of Troy and won the war? You're certainly taking your time getting home, aren't you?

ODYSSEUS   I would have been home by now if I hadn't taken that wrong turn.

QUEEN ARETE   This sounds like it's going to be good, dear. Just like in the movies.

PRINCESS NAUSICAA   What's a movie?

(Lights dim. A spotlight is on ODYSSEUS. HOMER and NARRATOR exit and ODYSSEUS narrates his own story. Throughout, he acts out his adventures.)

ODYSSEUS   After leaving Troy, my men and I set sail toward Ithaca, but the winds sweep us to Ismarus, city of the Cicones. It's a great town, but we get a little carried away and plunder the land. Everything is fine until those Cicones turn up. They aren't very happy with us, and we are outnumbered. We flee but not before losing six men from each of my ships. We continue on and end up landing on the shore of—

(SAILORS enter.)

SAILOR   Hey, look! Those huge dudes have only one big eye in the middle of their heads!

ODYSSEUS *(To his audience.)* They're Cyclopes! We decide to explore, to hopefully get more supplies. We are excited to find a cave full of sheep, cheese, and milk.

(To his SAILORS.) Men, let's grab a few things and get out of here fast!

(Enter the cyclops POLYPHEMUS.)

POLYPHEMUS Hello?

ODYSSEUS Hello! Who might you be?

POLYPHEMUS I am Polyphemus. What are you doing in my home?

ODYSSEUS We were just, uh, admiring, uh, the cave?

POLYPHEMUS Why, thank you, I decorated it myself.

ODYSSEUS *(To his audience.)* He is perfectly friendly until he eats two of my men! *(The crowd gasps.)* Then he captures the rest of us!

POLYPHEMUS Yum, yum! You'll make a great meal!

(POLYPHEMUS rolls a giant boulder to block the cave exit.)

Ha-ha, now you can't escape! Time to tend to my sheep.

(POLYPHEMUS exits.)

ODYSSEUS *(To SAILORS.)* That boulder is huge—we'll never be able to budge it. If we're ever going to get out, we have to be smarter than the Cyclops.

(Back to his audience.) I find a big wooden stick and then come up with a plan.

(He grabs a long wooden stick and whispers to his SAILORS. Enter POLYPHEMUS.)

POLYPHEMUS I'm baaaack!

ODYSSEUS   Good, we were waiting for you. Let's have a party!

POLYPHEMUS   A party? That's a great idea!

ODYSSEUS   We have punch and food for you.

POLYPHEMUS   You're the nicest meal I've ever almost eaten. What's your name?

ODYSSEUS   My name is Noman.

POLYPHEMUS   Nice to meet you, Noman. Thanks for the punch, but, boy-oh-boy, am I sleepy! Goodnight.

(He yawns and lies down.)

ODYSSEUS   *(To his audience.)*   I grab the wooden staff and...

(He runs toward POLYPHEMUS holding the staff and pokes him in the eye with it.)

POLYPHEMUS   *(With both hands covering his eye.)* OW! OW! OW!

ODYSSEUS   *(To his audience.)*   ...poke him in the eye with it!

POLYPHEMUS   Help! Help me!

(Other CYCLOPES come running to POLYPHEMUS's aid.)

CYCLOPS ONE   What's wrong?

POLYPHEMUS   Noman poked me in the eye! Noman did this!

CYCLOPS TWO   Oh, nobody did this to you? Okay, well sorry about your accident. Hope you feel better. See ya.

(Other CYCLOPES exit.)

ODYSSEUS   *(To his audience.)*   Polyphemus still needs to tend to his flock even though he can't see. Well, as he moves the boulder away, each of my men clings to the underside of one of his sheep. When the animals leave the cave to graze, we drop and run to our ships as fast as we can. We are home free...until I make a huge mistake.

POLYPHEMUS *(Walking and waving his hands out in front of him, blindly trying to find ODYSSEUS.)* Come back, Noman, come back!

ODYSSEUS *(Yelling over his shoulder as he runs to the ship.)* My,..name...is...really...Odysseus!

(HOMER and NARRATOR enter.)

HOMER A clever man, that Odysseus.

NARRATOR Yes, but unfortunately for Odysseus, Polyphemus is the son of...Poseidon!

HOMER And now you know why Poseidon is so angry at Odysseus.

(POLYPHEMUS exits.)

BOOK 10

HOMER So off Odysseus sails—into Book 10!

(HOMER points to the audience.)

Fill them in on where Odysseus goes next, but then let's continue to relax while Odysseus tells his own story to King Alcinous. It's more fun that way.

NARRATOR *(Indicating the "Book 10" sign.)* Odysseus and his men sail to the island home of Aeolus, ruler of the winds.

(Enter AEOLUS. HOMER and NARRATOR exit.)

AEOLUS *(Holding out a big bag toward ODYSSEUS.)* Take this big bag of winds.

ODYSSEUS There's no need to be insulting.

AEOLUS No, no...take it. It's an actual bag of winds.

ODYSSEUS *(Reaching out and taking the bag.)* Oh! Cool.

AEOLUS Use them to sail with. You'll be home in no time.

(He exits.)

ODYSSEUS *(To his audience.)* We sail for ten days straight until suddenly, we spot Ithaca on the horizon!

ODYSSEUS *(Back to acting out his adventures.)* Land—

SAILOR ONE *(Opening the bag of winds.)* What's in here?

ODYSSEUS Noooooooo!

(ODYSSEUS and SAILORS get blown back to sea.)

Drat! Now we're all the way back to—

AEOLUS *(Entering and looking surprised.)* What are you doing back here?

ODYSSEUS Um, you wouldn't happen to have another one of those big wind bags, would you?

AEOLUS Sorry, one per customer. *(He exits.)*

ODYSSEUS *(To his audience.)* No wind means we can't sail our ships. So we have no choice—my men have to row. And row. And row. Finally we find another island.

SAILOR TWO *(Spying an island.)* Land ho—no!

ODYSSEUS *(Not so happily.)* A land of giants! Again with the giant people!

(GIANTS enter.)

GIANT ONE *(Waving.)* We'd really like to have you for dinner!

ODYSSEUS *(To his audience.)* We sail away as quickly as we can.

GIANT TWO *(GIANTS throw big rocks at ODYSSEUS's ships.)* Don't go! We have these nice, big rocks for you!

SAILOR ONE They're throwing big rocks at us!

ODYSSEUS Fortunately, my ships escape safely.

SAILOR TWO *Ship.* Your *ship* escapes.

ODYSSEUS What?!

SAILOR THREE Just the one made it, sir.

ODYSSEUS Double drat! Well, sail on, then!

(Enter a beautiful woman, CIRCE, waving at ODYSSEUS from her island.)

CIRCE Yoo-hoo!

ODYSSEUS Well, well…and you are?

CIRCE My name is Circe—come on over!

ODYSSEUS *(To his audience.)* We sail to the island of Aeaea where we are greeted by the beautiful and mysterious woman, Circe.

(To CIRCE.) You sure are purty!

CIRCE Thank you, big O. Why don't you come ashore, kick off your shoes, and rest a bit. I bet you need a change of pork—uh, *pace*.

ODYSSEUS *(To his audience.)* We are having a great time until I realize what kind of change she has in mind for us. Circe is a powerful goddess, and as I'm resting, she captures some of my men and turns them into—pigs!

(ODYSSEUS grabs his sword and begins to charge towards CIRCE, but suddenly, HERMES enters and stops him.)

HERMES ExcusemebutIcanhelpyougetyourmenbackall you—

ODYSSEUS Stop, stop! You're talking way too fast again.

HERMES Oh, sorry. What I started to say was, "Excuse me, but I can help you get your men back." All you have to do is eat this plant. It will protect you from Circe's magic.

(HERMES holds out a plant and ODYSSEUS takes it from him and eats it.)

ODYSSEUS *(Making a face.)* Needs a little salt.

(HERMES exits as ODYSSEUS lunges at CIRCE and captures her.)

Change my men back. Now!

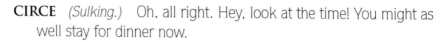

CIRCE *(Sulking.)* Oh, all right. Hey, look at the time! You might as well stay for dinner now.

ODYSSEUS *(To CIRCE.)* Don't mind if I do. But I promise we'll be gone in two weeks.

(To his audience.) We are so tired from all of our adventures and close calls that we end up spending an entire year on Aeaea. Then my crew starts begging me to resume our journey home.

(To CIRCE.) You wouldn't happen to know how to get to Ithaca, would you?

CIRCE I am really bad with directions. The only thing I can suggest to help you find out the way is to go to, um, the Underworld.

(Enter HOMER.)

HOMER *(To the audience.)* In ancient times, most people believed there was a world of the living and a world of the dead. Zeus ruled the earth; his brother, Poseidon, ruled the seas; and his other brother, Hades, ruled the Underworld—where you went when you died.

(HOMER moves off to the side.)

CIRCE Ask for Tiresias—I hear he's pretty good with directions.

(Exit CIRCE.)

BOOK 11

(NARRATOR enters, stands next to HOMER, and shows "Book 11" sign.)

HOMER Book 11! Oooo, this is the creepy and mysterious part.

(NARRATOR and HOMER move to side of stage.)

ODYSSEUS *(To his audience.)* We sail away and follow the river Oceanus until we reach the outskirts of the Underworld. By following Circe's instructions we are able to find Tiresias.

(Enter TIRESIAS, the blind prophet.)

TIRESIAS What? Who's bothering me? *(He reaches out and feels ODYSSEUS's face.)* Oh, it's you, Odysseus. I was enjoying a good game of shuffleboard until you came along. What do you want?

ODYSSEUS Can you help me find my way back to Ithaca?

TIRESIAS Yes, I know the way…but it's not going to be easy. There's a rumor you made Polyphemus's father very unhappy with that eye-poking incident.

ODYSSEUS That Cyclops has a father? Who is it?

TIRESIAS None other than Poseidon, King of the Seas!

(ODYSSEUS shakes his head in disbelief.)

Don't worry, though, you'll make it home soon enough. Just be really careful.

ODYSSEUS Whew, that's relief! I've had about as much adventure as I can take.

TIRESIAS Just one thing, Big O. On your way back, you will sail to the land of Thrinacia. Let me give you a little advice.

(Emphatically.) Whatever you do, when you are there, DO. NOT. TOUCH. THE. SHEEP. OR. THE. COWS. THEY. BELONG. TO. THE. SUN. Don't even go near them. It'll just make it harder to get to home if you do. No joke.

ODYSSEUS *(To his audience.)* Tiresias wasn't the only soul I spoke to down there. Many more who had passed on to the Underworld came to speak with me. Please forgive me for not reeling off the whole list, but I'm quite tired, and it's a *long* list. I had to shake all their hands, and boy, did my fingers get sore! Any chance we can have dessert and call it a night?

QUEEN ARETE And not hear the epic conclusion? You can't keep us waiting like that! I'll never get to sleep!

ODYSSEUS *(Sighing.)* Oh, all right. Let's see… I saw my mother, Anticleia, and Achilles, the great warrior of the Trojan War. Menelaus's brother Agamemnon came next, and then Ajax, who wouldn't speak to me—we had this big fight back during the Trojan War and he's still mad at me.

Some people hold a grudge forever. There was also Heracles, mortal son of Zeus; King Minos of Crete; Orion the hunter; and a whole bunch of other folks.

KING ALCINOUS   That is a long list!

PRINCESS NAUSICAA   Did you see Sisyphus?

ODYSSEUS   *(Nodding his head.)*   Yes. As punishment for something Sisyphus did, Hades makes him push a huge boulder uphill, but then just when it's about to go over the top, it rolls back down to the bottom. So then he has to start again. He has to do this over and over for all of eternity.

PRINCESS NAUSICAA   Oooh…that's got to be frustrating.

ODYSSEUS   Yes, but Tantalus…

QUEEN ARETE   What about him?

ODYSSEUS   Well, Tantalus made his father, Zeus, and some of the other gods angry. His punishment is to sit in a pool of water with grapes hanging all around. But every time he reaches for a grape, the vines rise just out of his grasp. And every time he tries to drink from the pool, the water drains out of reach.

PRINCESS NAUSICAA   So he is "tantalized" over and over again!

ODYSSEUS   So many dead people wanted to talk to us that it became overwhelming. We fled to our ships and sailed away.

BOOK 12

HOMER   Which brings us to Book 12!

NARRATOR   *(Holds up "Book 12" sign.)*   Will I ever get to narrate again?

HOMER   Yes, of course you will. There's much more that you'll be guiding us through.

(All exit except for ODYSSEUS, who continues his narration.)

ODYSSEUS *(To audience.)* We leave the Underworld and sail back to Circe's island to rest up.

(Enter CIRCE).

CIRCE Back so soon?

ODYSSEUS Just for a minute.

CIRCE I've heard *that* before. Well, stay for a minute and I'll tell you a few things you should know about the rest of your journey.

(CIRCE whispers in ODYSSEUS's ear.)

ODYSSEUS *(Looking shocked.)* No!

CIRCE Yes!

(She whispers more to him.)

Now I will say goodbye. Don't forget what I've told you!

(ODYSSEUS boards his ship. SAILORS are already aboard.)

ODYSSEUS And we're off!

SAILORS Next stop, Ithaca!

ODYSSEUS Okay, so this might sound a little strange but I need you guys to take these ropes and tie me to the mast. Hurry! We're approaching the Isle of Sirens! And put beeswax in your ears.

(SAILORS tie up ODYSSEUS and then put wax in their ears.)

Whatever you do, don't set me free, no matter what I say or how hard I beg. Okay? Wait! Do you hear that?

(Pretty soft singing can be heard—the call of the SIRENS. It gradually gets louder. ODYSSEUS starts to struggle, trying to free himself.)

SAILOR ONE *(Yelling.)* Hear what?

SAILOR TWO *(Yelling.)* Can't hear you—I have wax in my ears.

ODYSSEUS Untie me! Let me go to them—they are calling to me! Please! Please! Please!

SAILOR THREE *(Yelling.)* Did you say something?

ODYSSEUS *(To audience.)* They do exactly as I've asked and don't untie me. Filling their ears with beeswax has prevented my crew from hearing the beautiful call of the Sirens. It's a dangerous thing to hear, because it lures sailors toward their island, the sharp rocks, and death. Men can't help themselves when they hear it—it drives them crazy. But eventually, my ship gets far enough away so that we can no longer hear the Sirens' call. I calm down, and my men free me.

(To his SAILORS.) That was amazing! Let's go back!

SAILOR ONE *(Yelling.)* What?

ODYSSEUS You can take the wax out of your ears now. Here, let me do it.

(Leans over and pulls wax from SAILOR's ears.)

SAILOR TWO *(Spying more danger ahead and pointing at it.)* Look!

ODYSSEUS *(To audience.)* There before us is still more danger! We have to sail through a narrow, dangerous passage with not one but *two* monsters on either side of the ship!

(The SCYLLA appears.)

(To audience.) On one side, the long-necked, six-headed monster, Scylla, is hiding in a cave above my ship. On the other side, the ship-swallowing Charybdis awaits us!

SAILOR THREE Wow, that Charybdis is one huge whirlpool!

ODYSSEUS *(To audience.)* The dangerous whirlpool is big enough to swallow our ship. But Circe has said that if we sail close to the cliffs we'll be safe. Still, though, we have to watch out for— *(turns to SAILORS)* —LOOK OUT!

(The SCYLLA attacks, and ODYSSEUS and the SAILORS battle it.)

We manage to fight off the monster, but not before the Scylla takes six of my men—one for each of its heads.

SAILOR ONE   Never a dull moment around here!

SAILOR TWO   Boy, am I tired, boss. Can we sail over to that island and rest up a bit before continuing on?

ODYSSEUS   *(Shaking his head.)*   We really need to—

ALL SAILORS   Please, please, please!

(ODYSSEUS and SAILORS land on the island.)

ODYSSEUS   Okay, fine, we'll stop for a little while, but listen carefully. This is the island of Thrinacia. The Sun tends its flocks of sheep and cattle here.

(ODYSSEUS says the next line the same way TIRESIAS did.)

Whatever you do, DO. NOT. TOUCH. THE. SHEEP. OR. THE. COWS.

SAILOR ONE   You worry too much, Big O. We promise not to touch the sheep or the cows.

ODYSSEUS *(To the audience.)* So we stop for a short time. But then a powerful storm hits and prevents us from sailing on. A whole month passes, and we run out of food.

SAILOR TWO Wow, I sure am hungry.

SAILOR THREE Look! Cows!

SAILOR ONE If we take just one…

SAILOR TWO No one will ever know.

SAILOR THREE *(Yelling.)* What? I can't hear you! I've got wax—

ODYSSEUS *(Catching SAILORS taking cattle.)* What are you doing?! You've gone and touched the cows when I specifically told you not to! You promised! The cows belong to the Sun, so now we're in big trouble. Get your things, we're sailing tonight.

(Continuing his narration to audience.) We sail away from Thrinacia peacefully, but the Sun complains to Zeus.

(Enter THE SUN and ZEUS.)

THE SUN   Hey, they touched my cows. That is so not cool.

ZEUS   These kids just never listen.

ODYSSEUS   *(To the audience.)*   As punishment, Zeus kicks up a huge storm, which tosses my ship back and forth and back and forth until it breaks apart! My entire crew drowns. I am the only survivor.

(ZEUS and THE SUN exit.)

I float in the water for a few days, barely escaping the Charybdis a second time, until I—

(The palace setting appears again, along with the royal family, HOMER, and the NARRATOR.)

QUEEN ARETE   — wash up on an island, where Calypso holds you captive!

ODYSSEUS   *(To the royal family.)*   Exactly. Calypso keeps me there for over seven years. Finally I'm released and make my way here. Ten years of the Trojan War and ten years of wandering—it's been a long time since I have seen my home and family.

BOOK 13

(Enter HOMER and NARRATOR.)

HOMER   It's time for Book 13.

(NARRATOR shows "Book 13" sign while covering his mouth with his other hand—he wants to talk but thinks he isn't supposed to.)

KING ALCINOUS   Ithaca is just one day's journey from here. Take this ship and crew and leave tonight. You'll be home in no time.

ODYSSEUS   Thank you, sir.

NARRATOR   *(To HOMER.)*   Can I talk now?

(HOMER nods yes. NARRATOR speaks to the audience.)

The Phaeacian crew sails Odysseus right to the shores of his homeland, Ithaca.

ODYSSEUS   This doesn't look like Ithaca. Something fishy is going on. Is this a joke?

HOMER   Enter—

(Athena enters, disguised as a shepherd.)

ATHENA AS SHEPHERD   It's no joke, kind sir. This is Ithaca.

ODYSSEUS   Who are you?

ATHENA AS SHEPHERD   It's just little ol' me, Athena!

(She reveals her true self to ODYSSEUS.)

Don't worry, I've been guiding you at every turn. You still have one huge obstacle to overcome but then you're home free. You see, you've been gone so long that everyone thinks you're dead. Many suitors have tried to marry Penelope and take your place as ruler, but she's remained faithful and believes that you will return. You have to help her get rid of these horrible men.

ODYSSEUS   How?

ATHENA   First, find your father's old friend, the shepherd Eumaeus, and hide in his hut for now. Your son Telemachus—

ODYSSEUS   My son!

ATHENA   —has been looking for you. He's all grown up now, and a pretty decent young man. I will disguise you as an old beggar until you figure out how to deal with this suitor problem.

(ATHENA disguises ODYSSEUS as an old beggar by putting a ratty coat on him, and exits.)

BOOK 14

(NARRATOR shows "Book 14" sign.)

HOMER Here we go—right into Book 14!

(NARRATOR and HOMER move off to side of stage as EUMAEUS enters.)

ODYSSEUS AS OLD BEGGAR Excuse me, Eumaeus?

EUMAEUS You are excused.

ODYSSEUS AS OLD BEGGAR No, I mean, are you Eumaeus?

EUMAEUS I might be. Who are you?

ODYSSEUS AS OLD BEGGAR I'm…uh…an old soldier. From Crete. Yes, I'm an old soldier from Crete just trying to make my way home after fighting in the Trojan War.

EUMAEUS That old thing? That war's been over for ten years! You are certainly taking your time! In fact, the only person I know who's taking as long as you is Odysseus.

ODYSSEUS AS OLD BEGGAR Odysseus? Ruler of Ithaca? Great warrior? Fearless husband? Honored father of—?

EUMAEUS Yes, yes, yes—I see you've heard of him.

ODYSSEUS AS OLD BEGGAR Yes, I've heard all about him. In fact, I fought alongside him during the war. He was in charge, of course. Quite the amazing man, don't you think?

EUMAEUS Amazing doesn't even begin to describe the greatest ruler this land has ever seen! He was such a good guy, Odysseus. A real hero! Not like those whippersnappers up in the palace trying to take his place. Sit down, smelly old beggar. You look hungry—eat!

(He hands ODYSSEUS a bowl of food.)

I fear we've seen the last of Odysseus though. Too much time has passed for him to still be living.

ODYSSEUS AS OLD BEGGAR You never know, old shepherd, he could be just about anywhere.

EUMAEUS Well, he's not here, is he? So don't go saying things that you don't know are true. People keep telling Queen Penelope that Odysseus is still alive. But they are just trying to butter her up because they want money from her. They don't actually know a thing about what happened to Odysseus. So don't you start, too. Penelope is a nice woman who doesn't deserve to have people trying to take advantage of her.

ODYSSEUS AS OLD BEGGAR I won't do anything, I promise.

EUMAEUS You bet you won't. Hmmm…I like you, you old geezer. It's nice to have company out here in the fields.

ODYSSEUS AS OLD BEGGAR Yes, indeed it is. Odysseus himself kept me company in the fields one cold, snowy night near Troy. I had forgotten my warm cloak, but he managed to get me another one. You know, I have heard that Odysseus is alive and on his way back here.

EUMAEUS Well, I will be as kind to you as Odysseus was, even if I don't believe you about his whereabouts.

(Hands ODYSSEUS a blanket.)

Here, take this blanket and sleep here tonight. Like, over there. A little further. *(ODYSSEUS inches away.)* A little further…. There, perfect! You have a good night, old man.

(ODYSSEUS and EUMAEUS lie down and sleep. NARRATOR and HOMER move back to center stage.)

NARRATOR So, Odysseus is back in Ithaca, but no one knows he's there. How is he ever going to overcome the suitors?

HOMER Well, perhaps you should pick back up where we left off with Telemachus, his son.

NARRATOR I think we left him in Sparta, right?

BOOK 15

(NARRATOR shows "Book 15" sign.)

HOMER   Sparta it is. Book 15!

(Enter TELEMACHUS and PISISTRATUS. They lie down on beds and go to sleep. Enter ATHENA.)

NARRATOR   Athena leaves Odysseus with Eumaeus and his pigs, and she travels quickly to Sparta where she knows Telemachus is still in the care of King Menelaus and Queen Helen. She finds him tossing and turning in the same room with Pisistratus.

(HOMER and NARRATOR move to side stage. PISISTRATUS is snoring.)

ATHENA   Yoo-hoo! Telemachus!

TELEMACHUS   Am I dreaming?

ATHENA   Can you hear the human chainsaw in the corner over there?

(TELEMACHUS nods yes.)

Well then, you aren't dreaming. Whoa, that's loud! Now get up and get moving—it's time for you to get back to Ithaca before one of those gross suitors ends up marrying your mom.

TELEMACHUS   Really? Yikes!

ATHENA   Now listen carefully. Those suitors are going to try to ambush you when you get close to home. Do yourself a favor— stay away from the islands off the coast from Ithaca and you'll be safe. Hurry onto shore and send your men into the city, but don't go to the palace yourself. Instead, I want you to find the shepherd, Eumaeus   *(ATHENA winks at the audience.)*   and hide out there for a short while. Toodles!

TELEMACHUS   Hey, Pi! Get up! We gotta get going—

(KING MENELAUS and QUEEN HELEN enter, and TELEMACHUS waves to them.)

— back to Ithaca, sir. Thank you for everything you've done for us.

PISISTRATUS   Road trip!

(They both board a chariot and begin their journey. QUEEN HELEN Looks up and sees something flying in the sky and heading toward TELEMACHUS.)

QUEEN HELEN   Look! An eagle. With a…is that a goose it's carrying?

KING MENELAUS   And flying so close to Telemachus's chariot!

QUEEN HELEN   I'd say that's a sign that Odysseus will soon swoop down upon his house.

KING MENELAUS   Or else it's just a kooky eagle.

QUEEN HELEN   *(Nodding.)*   Or else it's just a kooky eagle.

(KING MENELAUS and QUEEN HELEN exit. TELEMACHUS and PISISTRATUS stop their chariot.)

TELEMACHUS   Here we are back in Pylos, Pi—your home, sweet home. And here's my ship. This is where we say goodbye.

(PISISTRATUS gets off the chariot.)

Thank your dad, King Nestor, for all his help. I have to get home now!

PISISTRATUS   Water trip!

(PISISTRATUS exits as TELEMACHUS boards his ship.)

TELEMACHUS *(Exiting.)*   Sail! Sail on!

NARRATOR   Meanwhile, back in Ithaca at the hut.

(EUMAEUS and ODYSSEUS awake.)

EUMAEUS   Good morning, smelly old beggar!

ODYSSEUS AS OLD BEGGAR   Morning, kind pig herder. I thank you for your hospitality, and I won't put you out any longer. I'll just go and find work with those suitors you mentioned. I'm sure—

EUMAEUS Absolutely not! Not now, not ever. Don't you dare go and mix yourself up with those hoodlums. You can stay here as long as you need to.

ODYSSEUS AS OLD BEGGAR Okay, twist my arm…I'll stay!

EUMAEUS You know, I came to Ithaca not unlike you—all ragged and tattered. My father was a king, but I was stolen from our house by pirates with the help of one of our maids. The pirates sailed to Ithaca, and there, Odysseus's father, King Laertes, found me and raised me. I was treated no differently than one of their own.

NARRATOR Now that's a sad story turned happy.

BOOK 16

(NARRATOR holds up "Book 16" sign.)

HOMER And so begins Book 16!

(HOMER and NARRATOR move off to side stage. TELEMACHUS and PIRAEUS, a sailor, enter in their ship.)

TELEMACHUS Finally, I am home safe and sound. Piraeus, take everyone to the palace and tell only my mother, Penelope, that I have arrived. I'll be along soon enough.

(PIRAEUS gets off ship and exits. TELEMACHUS gets off ship and enters EUMAEUS's hut.)

Eumaeus! Eumaeus! Ah, there you are. I need your help but— *(Spotting ODYSSEUS AS BEGGAR.)* —who are you?

ODYSSEUS AS OLD BEGGAR I'm—

EUMAEUS He's a smelly old beggar who fought alongside your father in the Trojan War. Perhaps you can help him when you reach the palace?

TELEMACHUS I'd be honored to help anyone who knew my father, but I'm not sure that would be too wise, Eumaeus. I have only just escaped a trap by the suitors, and I don't think this old man would be of much help to me.

EUMAEUS A trap! Those scallywags!

TELEMACHUS Yes, they certainly are.

EUMAEUS Perhaps I should go to the palace for you? And tell only your mother that you have returned safely?

TELEMACHUS Exactly what I was thinking.

(EUMAEUS exits.)

ODYSSEUS AS OLD BEGGAR So.

TELEMACHUS So.

(A few seconds of silence during which both men look uncomfortable. Finally ODYSSEUS hears ATHENA calling from outside the hut.)

ODYSSEUS AS OLD BEGGAR You hear that?

TELEMACHUS Hear what?

ODYSSEUS AS OLD BEGGAR I'll just be a moment.

(ODYSSEUS exits the hut. ATHENA is waiting for him. She removes ODYSSEUS's disguise then exits. ODYSSEUS reenters the hut as himself.)

Son?

TELEMACHUS *(Pointing to himself.)* Son? Me? Wait…Dad?

(A look of shock and realization comes over TELEMACHUS's face.)

Dad!!

(He runs and hugs ODYSSEUS.)

It's you! It's really you!

ODYSSEUS Good to see you, son! You have grown up well. A fine son, you are!

TELEMACHUS I can't believe it's really you!

ODYSSEUS Look how big you are! I bet you've earned the respect of all Ithaca, haven't you?

TELEMACHUS   All but those suitors of Mom's.

ODYSSEUS   Right. I keep hearing about them. First things first—let me tell you what's happened to me, son.

(NARRATOR walks to center stage to speak, then back to side stage after.)

NARRATOR   And so Odysseus tells Telemachus the tale of his long, strange journey back. Then for the first time, they work together as a father and son team to plot how best to rid the palace of the suitors. Meanwhile, Eumaeus makes his way to Queen Penelope.

(Exit ODYSSEUS and TELEMACHUS. Enter EUMAEUS, PENELOPE, and the SUITORS.)

EUMAEUS   Hello, my Queen.

PENELOPE   Good to see you, Eumaeus. How are you?

EUMAEUS   I'm fine, thanks. I have some news, but I should tell you in—   *(Enter PIRAEUS.)*

PIRAEUS   The ship carrying the prince, Telemachus, has arrived!

EUMAEUS   Dang it, I was going to tell you first. Well, nice to see you, Penelope.

(EUMAEUS and PIRAEUS exit.)

ANTINOUS   *(Whispering.)*   Drat!

AMPHINOMUS   *(Whispering.)*   Drat!

EURYMACHUS   *(Whispering.)*   Drat!

AMPHINOMUS   *(Whispering.)*   Now what?

ANTINOUS   *(Whispering.)*   We should kill him before he tells the assembly that we must leave.

EURYMACHUS   *(Whispering.)*   Yes, yes, yes!

AMPHINOMUS   *(Whispering.)*   No, perhaps we should wait for the gods to give us a sign before we do something so...so...drastic.

(The SUITORS exit. NARRATOR and HOMER move to center stage.)

NARRATOR   Things are becoming a bit more treacherous now, aren't they?

(NARRATOR shows "Book 17" sign.)

HOMER   Sounds like it's time for Book 17!

(NARRATOR and HOMER exit. TELEMACHUS Enters.)

TELEMACHUS   Hi, Mom. I'm home!

PENELOPE   *(Very pleased.)*   Well, you came back fast, didn't you? Not at all like your father. I'll get your dinner—I've been keeping it warm.

(She exits and then enters again with a plate of food.)

Here, it's still warm, and I even brought you a whole new piece of bread! How was your trip, dear? I bet you're tired, aren't you?

TELEMACHUS   Oh, yes, but not so tired that I can't tell you that King Menelaus helped me find out that Dad is stuck on an island somewhere, and held captive by the sea nymph, Calpyso.

PENELOPE   Your father is on an island? Isn't that just like him to be at the beach instead of rushing home to me. Hmph!

TELEMACHUS   You never know, Mom—he could be just about—

(EUMAEUS appears off to the side with ODYSSEUS, who is once again disguised as the old beggar. They are on their way to the palace. TELEMACHUS and PENELOPE exit.)

EUMAEUS   Everywhere! These suitors are everywhere!

ODYSSEUS AS OLD BEGGAR   *(Aside, to the audience.)*   Athena disguised me as an old beggar again. That way no one at the palace will recognize me until I want them to. Cool, huh?

(To EUMAEUS.)   That may be true about the suitors, but it's time I get to the palace anyway. Thank you for returning to the hut and showing me the way.

(ODYSSEUS and EUMAEUS enter the palace grounds and are seen by the SUITORS, who enter from the other direction.)

ANTINOUS *(Throwing garbage at ODYSSEUS and laughing.)*
Welcome, old beggar!

AMPHINOMUS Hello, Eumaeus, good to see you. And a pleasure to meet you, smelly old beggar.

ANTINOUS Must you bring more disgusting beggars into the palace, Eumaeus? Aren't there already enough people here that beg and bother us relentlessly? What shame you bring on the house of Odysseus!

ODYSSEUS AS OLD BEGGAR What does it matter to you? You act like this is your house rather than Odysseus's. It is *you* who brings shame on the house of Odysseus!

ANTINOUS *(Picks up a chair and is about to hit ODYSSEUS with it.)*
You shall pay for saying—

AMPHINOMUS Stop! You really shouldn't pick on a beggar, Antinous. You never know when he might be a god or goddess in disguise. And then you'll be plenty sorry.

ANTINOUS Bah!

(The SUITORS move to one side of stage and talk amongst themselves. ODYSSEUS moves to side of stage, too. EUMAEUS goes to PENELOPE's bedroom on the other side of the stage. PENELOPE enters the room from the side. EUMAEUS whispers to PENELOPE.)

PENELOPE What? *(Few seconds pause.)* He what? *(Another pause.)* What happened then? *(Another pause.)* Well! Have the poor beggar come see me. I will ask if he has news of my husband, and if he does I'll give him a great new shirt—the latest fall fashion, no less. Maybe even a hat too, if he's really nice.

EUMAEUS *(Still whispering.)* He says he knows of Odysseus. He says he's wandering back home to Crete after fighting alongside Odysseus in the great war, and that he's heard your husband is alive.

PENELOPE Bring him to me, Eumaeus.

(EUMAEUS exits PENELOPE's room and goes to ODYSSEUS.)

EUMAEUS Penelope wants you to come see her so she can ask you about Odysseus. Now don't go telling her anything untrue, smelly old beggar.

ODYSSEUS AS OLD BEGGAR Tell her that I am happy to talk to her, but I shall wait until sundown to do so. Otherwise, the suitors might get suspicious. Besides, since I don't have a clean shirt I'll look better by candlelight.

(EUMAEUS goes back to PENELOPE.)

EUMAEUS He says—

PENELOPE Yes, I heard him. Well, isn't this strange beggar the smart one? Thank you, Eumaeus.

EUMAEUS Thank you, Queen Penelope.

(PENELOPE exits as EUMAEUS walks back ODYSSEUS.)

I must return to my hut for there is much pig herding to do. You be careful.

ODYSSEUS AS OLD BEGGAR Indeed I will, Eumaeus.

(Exit EUMAEUS. Enter HOMER and NARRATOR.)

HOMER Odysseus is a smart man to take these suitors by surprise.

NARRATOR They are a bit scary, though, don't you think?

HOMER I do. But after all his adventures and the trouble he's had, Odysseus isn't afraid of a few suitors.

NARRATOR Shall we go on?

BOOK 18

HOMER Yes, let's start Book 18.

(NARRATOR shows "Book 18" sign and then he and HOMER exit. Enter ARNAEUS THE BEGGAR. He approaches ODYSSEUS.)

ARNAEUS THE BEGGAR You look like a scrawny pup!

ODYSSEUS AS OLD BEGGAR Who are you?

ARNAEUS THE BEGGAR My name is Arnaeus, and I bet I could beat you in boxing!

ODYSSEUS AS OLD BEGGAR *(Winking at the audience.)* I don't know if I'm any good at boxing.

(Enter ATHENA.)

ATHENA Enter…me! Here's a little extra strength and stamina to get you through this.

(She waves her arm to make ODYSSEUS stronger, and then exits. ARNAEUS and ODYSSEUS begin to box. The SUITORS watch and egg them both on. ARNAEUS is no match for ODYSSEUS, and loses.)

AMPHINOMUS Well done, smelly old beggar. You are a testament to smelly old beggars everywhere.

ODYSSEUS AS OLD BEGGAR Thank you, suitor who is nicer than the other suitors.

AMPHINOMUS My name is Amphinomus.

ODYSSEUS AS OLD BEGGAR And that mean guy there is…?

AMPHINOMUS Antinous.

ODYSSEUS AS OLD BEGGAR I'm not too fond of that Antinous, but you I like. You might want to think about not being around, you know, later on.

AMPHINOMUS Why, smelly old beggar?

ODYSSEUS AS OLD BEGGAR Because I have this strange feeling that Odysseus is going to come home soon, and I just don't think you'll want to be here when that happens.

AMPHINOMUS Odysseus? Here? *(He laughs.)* Not only are you a good boxer, but you're a comedian, too! That was a good one, old smelly beggar!

(Enter PENELOPE with TELEMACHUS. Exit ARNAEUS.)

PENELOPE Hello, gentlemen.

SUITORS Hello, Queen Penelope.

AMPHINOMUS You're looking lovely today, Queen Penelope.

PENELOPE Thank you, Amphinomus. That was a lovely cake you baked me yesterday. Well, gentlemen, it's true that Odysseus said to me, before he left, that I should look for a new husband if he hadn't yet returned from war by the time my son started growing a beard…or something like that, anyway.

TELEMACHUS *(Feeling his chin.)* Huh?

PENELOPE Any suitor that's worth my consideration should be bringing me presents—lots and lots of presents—instead of taking everything I have.

(She gives Antinous a look and points to herself.)

Presents. For. Me.

(The SUITORS run around gathering stuff, and bring back presents to PENELOPE, who is filing her nails.)

ODYSSEUS AS OLD BEGGAR *(Catching a passing maidservant, MELANTHO, and whispering to her.)* Maybe you should gather all the maidservants and go help her.

MELANTHO Look, smelly old beggar man, I know how to do my job. And at least I don't smell stinky like you when I do it!

ODYSSEUS AS OLD BEGGAR *(Roaring.)* Then you'd better get going before I make you smell as bad as me!

MELANTHO *(Fleeing.)* Eeee!

(Enter HOMER and NARRATOR.)

HOMER Enter—

(Enter ATHENA.)

ATHENA Me again! I think I want Odysseus to get even angrier at these suitors. So if I "inspire" one of them to be a jerk to him—

(She waves her hand in front of EURYMACHUS, and then moves to side of stage to watch.)

EURYMACHUS You seem like a nice, smelly old beggar. Maybe you could make yourself useful by building a fence or planting a tree— but just make sure you do it somewhere else, okay?

(He scrunches up his nose as if he's smelled something terrible.)

ODYSSEUS AS OLD BEGGAR I have done more than build fences and plant trees, Eurymachus, while all you've done is sit here and take things that are not yours.

EURYMACHUS *(Picks up a chair and is about to hit ODYSSEUS with it.)* You shall pay for saying—

TELEMACHUS Stop! We don't have many chairs left, so quit breaking them. And enough with this arguing!

(He winks at ODYSSEUS. Exit PENELOPE, the SUITORS, and ATHENA.)

NARRATOR Things are getting more and more prickly, which brings us to the secret plotting of Odysseus and Telemachus.

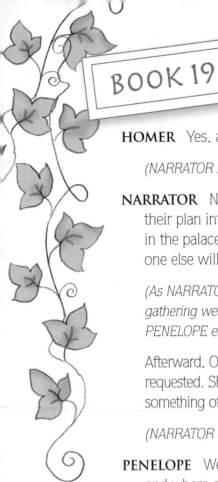

BOOK 19

HOMER Yes, and right into Book 19.

(NARRATOR shows "Book 19" sign.)

NARRATOR Night falls over Ithaca as Odysseus and Telemachus put their plan into action. They go about gathering up all the weapons in the palace. Then they store them in an unused room so that no one else will be able to find the weapons—especially the suitors.

(As NARRATOR speaks, TELEMACHUS and ODYSSEUS run around stage gathering weapons, then place them in a room. TELEMACHUS exits. PENELOPE enters and is in her bedroom. ODYSSEUS joins her.)

Afterward, Odysseus goes to meet Queen Penelope as she had requested. She is hopeful that this smelly old beggar might know something of her lost husband. Little does she know who he really is.

(NARRATOR and HOMER move to side of stage.)

PENELOPE Welcome, smelly old beggar. So tell me—who are you and where are you from?

ODYSSEUS AS OLD BEGGAR Originally I came from the island of Crete. My grandfather was King Minos, my father Deucalion— I am his youngest son, Aethon. Your husband arrived in Crete on his way to Troy and I—I mean, he—asked for my brother. But my brother had already sailed for Troy to fight, so I brought Odysseus and his crew into my home and showed him the hospitality I—I mean, he—deserved.

(PENELOPE begins to cry.)

NARRATOR Odysseus continues to tell Penelope tale after tale about Troy and Odysseus. But she is as clever as her husband and knows that just about anyone could claim to have been with Odysseus at some point without actual proof.

PENELOPE Well, I'm glad you were there to see all this, smelly old beggar. But I'm wondering if you can do me a favor by describing Odysseus to me.

(She stares at ODYSSEUS AS BEGGAR intently, challenging him.)

HOMER She's trying to trick him to see if he's lying.

ODYSSEUS AS OLD BEGGAR Sure, no problem. I—I mean, Odysseus—was wearing a double-lined cloak made of purple wool, and it was clasped together by a gold brooch. The brooch showed a dog hunting a deer on it. He also wore a shirt that clung to him nicely and made all the women swoon. Now, I don't know if he was wearing this clothing when he left here, or if this was something given to him by others—Odysseus seems to have had many friends who liked to give him gifts. I myself gave him a bronze sword, a long shirt, and another double-lined purple cloak.

PENELOPE *(Still crying.)* He does so love the color purple.

ODYSSEUS AS OLD BEGGAR Oooh, I do—I mean, oh, is that so?

PENELOPE Before you told me these things, smelly old beggar, I pitied you. But now I know you speak the truth. I gave Odysseus the cloak and the gold brooch before he left. Since you have proved you actually did see him, you are welcome to stay here in my house, even though I will never see my brave husband again!

(She cries more.)

ODYSSEUS AS OLD BEGGAR Don't cry, Queen Penelope. For during my travels I heard that Odysseus was wise and crafty. In fact, I believe he is probably on his way here to Ithaca as we speak, and will be here before you know it.

PENELOPE Oh, that is such a beautiful thing to say. I wish I could actually believe it! Thank you for coming, smelly old beggar, and for lifting my spirits. Here, you can sleep here on this bed—

ODYSSEUS AS OLD BEGGAR I hate to interrupt, beautiful Penelope, but I should sleep on the floor as all smelly old beggars do.

PENELOPE As you wish. My maid will now wash your dirty feet.

(PENELOPE goes to her bedroom at side of stage and begins to brush her hair. EURYCLEIA the maid enters carrying a basin of water. She motions to ODYSSEUS to come over. Reluctantly, he goes to her, and as he's about to put his feet into the basin, EURYCLEIA notices a scar on his foot.)

EURYCLEIA Such a big scar you have on your foot! I've only known one man with a scar like this and—

(She stops, looks at his face, and an expression of realization and surprise comes over her face.)

Odysseus! You're alive!

(EURYCLEIA throws her arms around ODYSSEUS and squeals with delight.)

ODYSSEUS Ssssh!

(PENELOPE hears the noise and starts to look over, but then ATHENA enters and distracts PENELOPE by brushing her hair for her—PENELOPE closes her eyes. With a nod and wink, EURYCLEIA silently promises ODYSSEUS that she will keep silent about his return. EURYCLEIA exits.)

PENELOPE Smelly old beggar?

ODYSSEUS AS OLD BEGGAR Yes?

PENELOPE I had a dream the other day. I dreamt that I was watching my pet geese when suddenly, this great, big eagle swooped down and killed them all. Then the eagle landed on my roof and said, "I am your husband, Odysseus, and the geese were your suitors." Isn't that weird? What do you think it means?

ODYSSEUS AS OLD BEGGAR Um…er…that your husband Odysseus will soon swoop down and scare all the suitors away?

PENELOPE *(Laughing.)* Oh, silly, smelly old beggar, it couldn't possibly mean that! Surely it's about the annoying corn on the cob I keep eating and how it always gets stuck in my teeth. Oh, if only it were true that Odysseus is coming back. But I guess I'll have to pick a suitor to marry instead.

ODYSSEUS AS OLD BEGGAR   Um, are you sure about that?

PENELOPE   Well, I don't really have a choice. But they're going to have to work hard for me. I will marry whichever suitor is able to shoot an arrow through the holes of twelve axe handles— just like my Odysseus used to do. That should stump them!

ODYSSEUS AS OLD BEGGAR   *(Smiling.)*   Indeed.

(The lights dim.)

HOMER   Why'd it get so dark?

NARRATOR   It's nighttime now, and both Odysseus and Penelope are sleeping.

BOOK 20

HOMER   Ah, so it must be Book 20.

(NARRATOR shows "Book 20" sign. ODYSSEUS and PENELOPE are both asleep but restless from their dreams. ATHENA watches over them both.)

ODYSSEUS AS OLD BEGGAR   Must—help—Telemachus. Must—get—rid of—suitors!

PENELOPE   Must—not—marry! Need—husband!   *(She awakens.)* Oh! What a terrible—

ODYSSEUS AS OLD BEGGAR   *(Waking up.)*   —dream I was having! Did I hear—Penelope?   *(Calling out to the skies.)*   Zeus? Zeus! Can't you give me a sign of good things to come?   *(A big clap of thunder is heard.)*   Thank you!

(PENELOPE gets out of bed and exits. ATHENA exits, too.)

NARRATOR   The next day, everyone is up bright and early in the palace, preparing for the big contest.

(TELEMACHUS, EUMAEUS, and the SUITORS enter.)

Odysseus, Telemachus, Eumaeus…even those pesky—

EUMAEUS   Suitors!

TELEMACHUS   Once again, they come to plague us!

ANTINOUS   Now, how shall we get rid of Telemachus today?
He's standing in the way of one of us marrying Penelope.

EURYMACHUS   An accident, perhaps?

AMPHINOMUS   Hey look up there in the sky! It's an eagle with a
dove in its talons!

EURYMACHUS   A mishap on the stairs, perhaps?

AMPHINOMUS   I don't want to be a spoil sport guys, but maybe we
should drop the Telemachus thing for a while. I don't like the looks
of that eagle there. It cannot be a good sign for us.

ANTINOUS   Well, who does like the way an eagle looks?
They've got those big noses and such. You are nothing but a
'fraidy cat, Amphinomous.

EURYMACHUS   *(Mooing in ODYSSEUS AS BEGGAR'S direction.)*
You should get moo-ving, smelly old beggar.

TELEMACHUS   Eurymachus, the only cow around here is—

ANTINOUS   Oh, stop your complaining, Telemachus. After all, one
of us could be your father soon!

*(SUITORS laugh while ODYSSEUS AS BEGGAR and EUMAEUS hold back
TELEMACHUS. The lights dim to a reddish glow—a sign from the gods
that the SUITORS will be in trouble soon.)*

BOOK 21

HOMER   We're getting closer to the big ending now, as we begin
Book 21.*(NARRATOR shows "Book 21" sign. Enter PENELOPE, holding
ODYSSEUS's bow.)*

PENELOPE   *(To the men gathered at the palace.)*   Hello, boys. Since you're all gathered around, it's only fair that I tell you what my plans are. I have decided that it is time get married again. But not just to anyone—to whomever can best string this bow and then fire an arrow in a straight line through the holes of twelve axes. Telemachus, if you would.

(TELEMACHUS begins to set up the axes in a row.)

Grab your arrows, boys. The only bow you'll be using is this one—Odysseus's!

(PENELOPE hands the bow to ANTINOUS.)

I'm still a bit tired, so I'll be going back to sleep now. Wake me when someone shoots the arrow successfully, Telemachus.

(PENELOPE exits.)

ANTINOUS   I'll string it!

AMPHINOMUS   No, let me!

(While the SUITORS struggle with trying to string the bow, ODYSSEUS takes EUMAEUS aside and whispers to him, TELEMACHUS listens.)

ODYSSEUS AS OLD BEGGAR   Do you trust me?   *(EUMAEUS nods yes.)*   So I shall trust you then as well.

(He shows him the scar on his foot.)

EUMAEUS   That scar—Odysseus has one just like it!

TELEMACHUS   *(Nudging EUMAEUS.)*   Duh!

ODYSSEUS   *(Revealing himself.)*   Yes, it is I, Odysseus. Swear to me that you will help me rid this palace of suitors, and I will treat you as though you are a brother to my son.

EUMAEUS   *(Happily.)*   Welcome home, my king!

(They all shake hands. ODYSSEUS puts his beggar disguise back on and the three men rejoin the suitors, who are still bickering.)

ANTINOUS   There's no way you're as strong as Odysseus.

EURYMACHUS   *(Failing to string the bow like all the others.)* Neither are you!

ANTINOUS Maybe we should call upon Apollo, the archer god, for some help.

ODYSSEUS AS OLD BEGGAR Maybe you should let me try.

ANTINOUS Oh, come now, smelly old beggar. If we can't string this bow then there's no way someone like you can.

AMPHINOMUS Don't let him—

TELEMACHUS I've had enough! You've all failed, so what do you care if an old beggar tries? Let him have the bow—now!

(ODYSSEUS easily strings the bow and fires an arrow.)

NARRATOR Odysseus takes the bow and strings it in one easy motion. The suitors are amazed. Then he fires the arrow toward the axes, and to the shock and horror of the suitors, the arrow sails through the axe handles!

BOOK 22

HOMER Which means it's time for Book 22!

(NARRATOR shows "Book 22" sign.)

ANTINOUS No way...that can't be!

EURYMACHUS He's just a smelly old—*(ODYSSEUS reveals himself to everyone.)*

AMPHINOMUS Odysseus!

(TELEMACHUS, EUMAEUS, and ODYSSEUS yell all at once and run at the SUITORS, chasing them around palace. The SUITORS run from them, screaming.)

EURYMACHUS Excuse me, pardon me... I was just doing some thinking, and I think you might have the wrong impression about my role in all of this. You see, I was just about to leave—I wasn't even going to try to win Penelope's hand in marriage. I swear.

(Yelling, ANTINOUS runs at ODYSSEUS, but ODYSSEUS side-steps him so ANTINOUS ends up running past him and off-stage. ANTINOUS

comes back, still yelling and running. Again, ODYSSEUS side-steps him. ANTINOUS comes at ODYSSEUS a third time but ODYSSEUS holds up his hand, stopping ANTINOUS in his tracks.)

ODYSSEUS   Wait.

ANTINOUS   What?

(ODYSSEUS bonks him on the head and ANTINOUS falls down. The other SUITORS are then chased around the stage until they are too tired to run anymore.)

AMPHINOMUS   *(Exhausted.)*   Okay, okay.   *(He wheezes.)*
We give up!   *(Wheezes again.)*

EURYMACHUS   *(Exhausted but pointing at the fallen ANTINOUS.)*
This was   *(wheeze)*   all   *(wheeze)*   his fault.   *(wheeze)*

(AMPHINOMUS and EURYMACHUS both fall down from exhaustion and crawl off stage. The rest of the SUITORS continue to be chased by ODYSSEUS, TELEMACHUS, and EUMAEUS. One by one, they flee the stage until they are all gone.)

HOMER   We're getting close to the end of our tale now, aren't we?

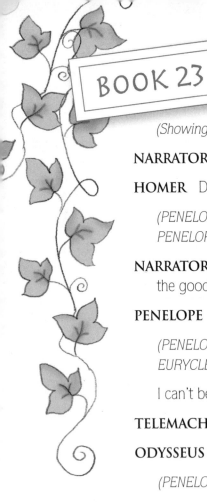

BOOK 23

(Showing the sign for "Book 23.")

NARRATOR Yes, we are. It's time for this book now.

HOMER Doh! You beat me to it. Book 23 it is!

(PENELOPE enters and goes to sleep. Enter EURYCLEIA, who wakes up PENELOPE.)

NARRATOR Eurycleia rushes to wake up Penelope, and tells her the good news.

PENELOPE I don't believe it! Are you serious?

(PENELOPE gets out of bed and runs to the palace grounds with EURYCLEIA. She sees ODYSSEUS and all the rest.)

I can't believe my eyes! Can it be? Is it really you, my husband?

TELEMACHUS Yes, Mom, of course it is!

ODYSSEUS Yes, Penelope, it is your husband, Odysseus!

(PENELOPE rushes to ODYSSEUS and hugs him.)

I can't wait to talk to you, but first, since we've had quite a battle, I think we should go to our country house until things calm down around here.

PENELOPE Wait. Are you sure this is Odysseus, Telemachus? Are you sure Poseidon or Zeus or somebody isn't playing a trick on me? Eurycleia! Have the servants move my bed to the country house—

ODYSSEUS *(Laughing.)* Ha-ha, very smart, Penelope. You and I both know that your bed is made from the trunk of an olive tree and can't be moved! I should know—after all, I'm the one who built it!

PENELOPE *(Hugging ODYSSEUS tightly.)* Oh, Odysseus, it is you! My dear husband, I'm so happy you have returned! And your dinner is almost entirely cold, you know—so hurry up inside!

ODYSSEUS First let me look at you. You are more beautiful than ever.

PENELOPE It took everything I could to fend off all those suitors, you know. All these years and so much worrying! Speaking of which, just where have you been?

ODYSSEUS It's a long tale, my love. Ten years of the Trojan War, and then when I finally left for home I, uh, got a little distracted along the way.

PENELOPE Distracted?

ODYSSEUS A few angry gods, some storms, a Cyclops or two, a—

PENELOPE This is going to be a long story isn't it?

HOMER That's okay, we can take it from here.

NARRATOR We can?

HOMER Well, there's a bit more of the story that I'd like to tell, but this is a good place for an ending. This way, everything ends on a positive note.

BOOK 24

NARRATOR "This way?" You mean there's another ending somewhere else?

HOMER Yes, but you'll have to read my poem to find out what happens in Book 24. Just think of this as a big cliff hanger!

NARRATOR *(To audience.)* So now you've heard Homer's tale about Odysseus: the troubles he encountered on his journey home, his many adventures, and his competition with and defeat of the suitors. You can read this epic poem another time....

HOMER Farewell...you've been a great audience and we hope you enjoyed the show!

(Lights dim.)

THE END

PRONUNCIATION KEY

ACHILLES *(uh-KIHL-eez)*

AEAEA *(ee-EE-uh)*

AEOLUS *(EE-oh-luss)*

AETHON *(EE-thon)*

AGAMEMNON *(AG-uh-MEM-non)*

AMPHINOMUS *(am-FIN-oh-mus)*

ANTICLEIA *(ant-ih-KLEE-uh)*

ANTINOUS *(an-TIN-uh-wuhs)*

ARNAEUS *(ar-NAY-us)*

ATHENA *(uh-THEE-nuh)*

CALLIOPE *(kah-LYE-uh-pee)*

CALYPSO *(kah-LIPS-oh)*

CHARYBDIS *(kah-RIB-dis)*

CICONES *(sih-COHN-eez)*

CIRCE *(SIR-see)*

CYCLOPES *(sy-KLOH-peez)*

CYCLOPS *(SY-klops)*

DEMODOCUS *(dee-MAH-duh-kus)*

DEUCALION *(dyoo-KAYL-yen)*

EUMAEUS *(yoo-MEE-us)*

EURYALUS *(yoo-REE-uh-lus)*

EURYCLEIA *(yoo-rih-KLEE-uh)*

EURYMACHUS *(yoo-RIM-uh-kuhs)*

HERACLES *(HER-uh-kleez)*

HERMES *(HER-meez)*

HOMER *(HO-mur)*

INO *(AY-no)*

IPHTHIME *(if-THEE-may)*

KING ALCINOUS *(al-SIN-oh-us)*

KING MENELAUS *(men-eh-LAY-us)*

LAESTRYGONIA *(lees-trih-GOH-nee-uh)*

MELANTHO *(meh-LAN-tho)*

ODYSSEUS *(oh-DIS-ee-us)*

OGYGIA *(oh-GIH-ghee-ah)*

PENELOPE *(pih-NEL-oh-pee)*

PHAEACIANS *(fee-AY-shunz)*

PIRAEUS *(pih-RAY-us)*

PISISTRATUS *(pye-sis-TRUH-tis)*

POLYPHEMUS *(pohl-ih-FEE-muhs)*

POSEIDON *(poh-SYE-dun)*

PRINCESS NAUSICAA *(naw-SIK-ay-uh)*

QUEEN ARETE *(a-REE-tee)*

SCHERIA *(SKEER-ee-uh)*

SCYLLA *(SILL-uh)*

SIRENS *(SYE-rinz)*

SISYPHUS *(SIS-uh-fuhs)*

TELEMACHUS *(tel-EM-uh-kus)*

THRINACIA *(thri-NAY-see-uh)*

TIRESIAS *(ty-REE-see-as)*

ZEUS *(ZOOS)*